an instant play m...

UKE'N
UKULELE

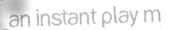

CW00553627

by mike jackson

WISE PUBLICATIONS
part of The Music Sales Group
London / New York / Paris / Sydney / Copenhagen /
Berlin / Madrid / Hong Kong / Tokyo

Published by
Wise Publications
14-15 Berners Street, London W1T 3LJ, UK.

Exclusive Distributors:
Music Sales Limited
Distribution Centre, Newmarket Road,
Bury St Edmunds, Suffolk IP33 3YB, UK.

Music Sales Pty Limited
4th floor, Lisgar House, 30-32 Carrington Street,
Sydney, NSW 2000, Australia.

Order No. AM1011604
ISBN: 978-1-78558-257-8
This book © Copyright 2016 Wise Publications,
a division of Music Sales Limited.

Created, compiled and edited by Mike Jackson, Diane Jackson Hill
and Flying Wombat Music, Melbourne, Australia 2005.
Cover design by Fresh Lemon (Aus).

Audio Tracks created by Toe Tapper Records.
Mike Jackson – vocals, ukulele, harmonica, concertina, melodeon, jaw harp and bones.
Diane Jackson Hill – ukulele and guitar.
Hugh McDonald – electric bass, guitar and mandolin.
Recorded at Hugh McDonald's Studio, Melbourne, Australia 2005.
Recorded, Engineered and Mixed by Hugh McDonald.

Printed in the EU.

CONTENTS

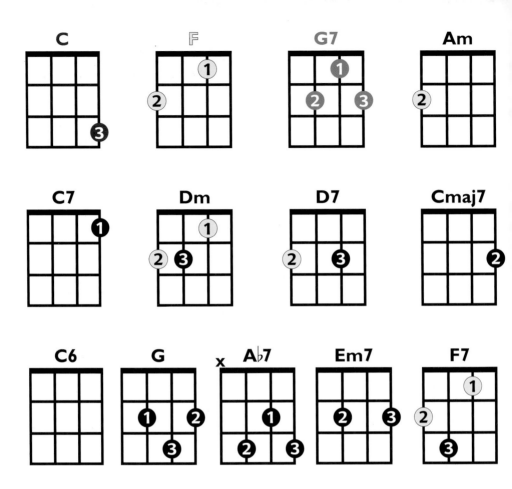

Practice Chord Patterns

Before playing any songs, try repeating these chord patterns with four strums on each chord. If this is difficult, play the patterns with eight strums on each chord, then four strums, then two, until your chord changes are fluent. If a particular chord change is giving you trouble, slow down your strumming and practise only that change until you are comfortable with it. Check out the 'Instant Play' method on page seven to make this easier.

1 C F F C
//// //// //// ////

2 C G7 G7 C
//// //// //// ////

3 C F C G7
//// //// //// ////

4 C F G7 C
//// //// //// ////

- Tuners
- Head
- Nut
- Fretboard
- Frets
- Sound Hole
- Bridge
- Saddle

Tuning GCEA

With Tuning Track (Track 27)

Play open* strings, starting from the string closest to your head and turn machine head until correct note is reached. The general rule is: turning the peg away from you makes the note higher in pitch and turning towards you makes the note lower - but you'll need to check by ear first.

* 'open' means no fingers pressing the strings to the fretboard

With a Piano

G - first G above middle C
C - middle C
E - first E above middle C
A - first A above middle C

G C E A

4 3 2 1

With Ukulele Pitch Pipe or Electronic Guitar Tuner (available from music stores)

Ask the shop staff to help you with the first tune-up. A clip-on guitar tuner is the best option as it takes only the note from your ukulele and is not affected by other sounds in the immediate area.

To remember the notes for tuning your uke: sing 'My Dog Has Fleas'

South Paws/Molly Dukers/ Left-Handers

Don't panic! You can easily change your ukulele into a left-handed instrument, by swapping the two middle strings over. The outside strings are the same thickness so these don't need to be swapped. Now tune your ukulele to AECG as shown in the diagram. Strum with your left hand and chord with your right. Your finger positions will be the reverse of those pictured for right-handers. N.B. Your ukulele will be facing the opposite direction to a right-hander!

A E C G

1 2 3 4

5

Mike Jackson's Instant Play Method

This system is simple - but it works! It helps you remember where to place your fingers and makes your chord changes much quicker.

Setting Up Your Ukulele

1. Buy a set of sticky coloured paper dots from a newsagency, or office/stationery supplier, and stick them onto the fretboard, <u>underneath</u> the strings, as shown here.
   You'll need red, yellow and green dots.

C	**F**	**G7**

2. Stick another dot (of any colour) on the back of the ukulele neck — behind the second fret. This is where your thumb goes!
3. Tune your ukulele — see previous page

Making Chords

Using your non-dominant hand, gently place your thumb — facing up, on the dot at the back of the fretboard.
Now use the tip of your fingers to gently press the strings onto the correct dots for the chord you are going to play. Make sure you use the correct finger for each dot and that your finger only touches the string that you are pressing down.

Finger numbering:
1 — index finger
2 — middle finger
3 — ring finger

UKE 'N PLAY CLUES

Strumming

Keep your strumming constant through the whole song, following the beat. Begin by using 'down' strums or a 'down-up-down-up' strum and play with the side of your thumb, back of your fingernail/s, or a felt pick which can be purchased from a music shop.

Strum Patterns (Track 26)

1 'down' strums

2 'down/up' strums

3 pick the 'G' or 4th string with the side of your thumb (or brush it with the back of your index finger) then play a 'down' strum with the back of your fingernail

4 play 'down-down/up-up/down' with the backs of your fingernail/s

The Play-along audio tracks can be used in many ways:

- To learn the lyrics and melody of the song
- To strum along with quietly while dampening* the strings (to get the strumming hand going)
- Just for fun, choose a '2-chord' song but leave your fingers in the 1st chord position and play only when that chord appears - or have a friend play the other chord in the same way on their own instrument, and alternate!
- Play as much of the song as you can along with the backing track - keep strumming even if you don't quite make the chords
- When you are up to speed, try singing and playing yourself, with the full band backing you on the karaoke tracks

  * to dampen strings place your fingers loosely across all strings so that they do not ring

Song Order

Songs are in order of difficulty, beginning with the easiest and finishing with the more complex ones. The book is designed to develop the player's skills in stages.

POLLY WOLLY DOODLE

Traditional. This arrangement by Mike Jackson.

F
Oh, I went down south for to see my gal, sing Polly Wolly Doodle all the day   C

                                                                     F
My Sal she is a saucy gal, sing Polly Wolly Doodle all the day

CHORUS:
F   C
Fare thee well, fare thee well, fare thee well, my fairy fay

For I'm goin' to Louisiana, for to see my Susyanna

                         F
Sing Polly Wolly Doodle all the day

                                        C
Fare thee well, fare thee well, farc thee well, my fairy fay

For I'm goin' to Louisiana, for to see my Susyanna

                         F
Sing Polly Wolly Doodle all the day

F   C
Grasshopper sitting on a railroad track, sing Polly Wolly Doodle all the day

                                                   F
He was picking his teeth with a carpet tack, sing Polly Wolly Doodle all the day

CHORUS

COCKLES AND MUSSELS

Traditional. This arrangement by Mike Jackson.

F   C

F
In Dublin's Fair City where girls are so pretty
F   **C**
I first set my eyes on sweet Molly Malone
    F   **C**
As she wheeled her wheel barrow, through streets broad and narrow
       F   **C**   **F**
Crying "Cockles and mussels alive, alive oh"

CHORUS:
F   **C**
Alive, alive oh, alive, alive oh
       F   **C**   **F**
Crying "Cockles and mussels alive, alive oh"

       F   **C**
Well she was a fishmonger and sure 'twas no wonder
   F   **C**
For so were her father and mother before
      F   **C**
And they both wheeled their barrows, through streets broad and narrow
       F   **C**   **F**
Crying "Cockles and mussels alive, alive oh"

CHORUS

     F   **C**
She died of a fever, which no one could save her
    F   **C**
And that was the end of sweet Molly Malone
      F   **C**
Now her ghost wheels her barrow, through streets broad and narrow
       F   **C**   **F**
Crying "Cockles and mussels alive, alive oh"

CHORUS

HUSH LITTLE BABY

Traditional. This arrangement by Mike Jackson.

C   G7

C   **G7**
Hush, little baby, don't say a word
                  C
Papa's gonna buy you a mockingbird

         G7
And if that mockingbird won't sing
                C
Papa's gonna buy you a diamond ring

         G7
And if that diamond ring turns brass
                C
Papa's gonna buy you a looking glass

         G7
And if that looking glass gets broke
                C
Papa's gonna buy you a billy goat

         G7
And if that billy goat won't pull
                C
Papa's gonna buy you a cart and bull

         G7
And if that cart and bull fall down
                C
You'll still be the sweetest little baby in town

SHORTNIN' BREAD

Traditional. This arrangement by Mike Jackson.

Play 2 strums only on G7 before changing back to C

CHORUS:

C
Mamma's little babies love shortnin' shortnin'
                           G7   C
Mamma's little babies love shortnin' bread
C
Mamma's little babies love shortnin' shortnin'
                           G7   C
Mamma's little babies love shortnin' bread

C
Three little babies lyin' in bed
                  G7   C
Two were sick and the other half dead

Call for the doctor, the doctor said
                  G7   C
Give those babies some shortnin' bread

CHORUS

C
Put on the frying pan, put on the lid
                    G7   C
Mamma's gone make a little shortnin' bread

That isn't all she's gonna do
                  G7   C
She's gonna give her babies a big hug too

CHORUS

C
Mamma fed her babies on shortnin' bread
                  G7   C
She gave them a hug and they jumped out of bed

They danced in the kitchen, they danced in the hall
                  G7   C
Those three little babies were having a ball

CHORUS x 2

QUARTERMASTER'S STORE

Traditional. This arrangement by Mike Jackson.

C
There were rats, rats, as big as bloomin' cats, in the store, in the store `G7` `C`

There were rats, rats, as big as bloomin' cats, in the Quartermaster's Store `G7` `C`

CHORUS:

C   **F**
My eyes are dim I cannot see

            G7
I have not brought my specs with me

 C   **F**   **G7**   **C**
I have not brought my specs with me

C   **G7**   **C**
There were fleas, fleas, as big as bumble bees, in the store, in the store

                             G7   **C**
There were fleas, fleas, as big as bumble bees, in the Quartermaster's Store

CHORUS

C   **G7**   **C**
There was tea, tea, but not for you and me, in the store, in the store

                           G7   **C**
There was tea, tea, but not for you and me, in the Quartermaster's Store

CHORUS

JAMAICA FAREWELL

Words & Music Irving Burgie.

C   F   G7

C   **F**
Down the way where the nights are gay
       G7   **C**
And the sun shines gaily on the mountain top
               F
I took a trip on a sailing ship
       G7   **C**
And when I reached Jamaica I made a stop

CHORUS:
           C   **F**
But I'm sad to say, I'm on my way
G7   **C**
Won't be back for many a day

                       F
Me heart is down, me head is turning around
       G7   **C**
I had to leave a little girl in Kingston town

C   **F**
Down at the market you can hear
       G7   **C**
Ladies cry out while on their heads they bear
           F
Akee, rice, salt fish are nice
       G7   **C**
And the rum is fine any time of year

CHORUS

C   **F**
Sounds of laughter everywhere
       G7   **C**
And the dancing girls sway to and fro
           F
I must declare my heart is there
       G7   **C**
Though I've been from Maine to Mexico

CHORUS x 2

Practise chord sequence no. 4 (C F G7 C) then repeat it through the whole song. Try strum no. 4 when you have the chords mastered.

BILLY OF TEA

Traditional. This arrangement by Mike Jackson.

C
You can talk of your whisky or talk of your beer
    F   **C**

    G7
There's something much nicer that's waiting me here

C   **F**   **C**
It sits on the fire beneath the gum tree

    F   **G7**   **C**
Oh there's nothing much nicer than a billy of tea

    F   **G7**
So fill up your tumblers as high as you can

    C
But don't you dare tell me it's not the best plan

    F   **C**   **F**
You can let all your beer and your whisky flow free

C   **F**   **G7**   **C**
I'll stick to my darling old billy of tea

    F   **C**   **F**
You can let all your beer and your whisky flow free

C   **F**   **G7**   **C**
I'll stick to my darling old billy of tea

Try strumming in 3's: down-down-down

V V V

or pick-down-down (pick G or 4th string)

④ V V

HEY HO LITTLE FISHIES

Traditional. This arrangement by Mike Jackson.

    C   **F**   **C**
Well the crew are asleep and the oceans at rest
                              G7   **C**
And I'm singing this song to the one I love best

CHORUS:
  F   **C**   **G7**   **C**
Hey Ho Little fishies don't cry, don't cry
  F   **C**   **G7**   **C**
Hey Ho Little fishies don't cry, don't cry

    C   **F**   **C**
The anchor's away and the weather is fine
                         G7   **C**
And the captain's on deck hanging out extra line

CHORUS

    C   **F**   **C**
Little fish when he's caught well he fights like a whale
                    G7   **C**
And he threshes the water with his mighty tail

CHORUS x 2

This song is also in 3/4 timing so strum in the rhythm:
VVʌ Vʌ
down-down/up - down/up
or count
1 2 & 3 &

BOTANY BAY

Traditional. This arrangement by Mike Jackson.

C   G7   F

   C   G7   C
Farewell to old England forever
               F   G7
Farewell to my old pals as well
   C   G7   C   F
Farewell to the well known Old Bailey
       C   G7   C
Where I once used to cut such a swell

CHORUS:
C   G7   C
Singing Tooral li ooral li addity
               F   G7
Singing Tooral li ooral li ay
       C   G7   C   F
Singing Tooral li ooral li addity
         C   G7   C
And we're bound for Botany Bay

REPEAT CHORUS

Struggling with your uke or not getting a good sound? Seek help from www.mikejackson.com.au

BE KIND TO YOUR
WEBFOOTED FRIENDS

Traditional. This arrangement by Mike Jackson.
Music to the tune of 'The Stars and Stripes Forever' by Sousa.

C
Be kind to your webfooted friends

                                           G7
For that duck may be somebody's mother

Be kind to your friends in the swamp

              C   **F** **G7**
Where the weather is very domp!

             C
You may think that this is the end

Well it is!

        C   **F**
But then there's another

This is it!

HARD TIMES

Words & Music Stephen Foster. This arrangement by Mike Jackson.

C
Let us pause in life's pleasures and count its many **F** tears **C**

        G7   **C**
While we all sup sorrow with the poor

                              F   **C**
There's a song that will linger forever in our ears

        G7   **C**
Oh hard times come again no more

CHORUS:
C   **F** **C**
Tis the song, the sigh of the weary

                                G7
Hard times, hard times, come again no more

     C   **F**   **C**
Many days you have lingered around my cabin door

F **C**   **G7**   **C**
Oh hard times come again no more

C   **F**   **C**
While we seek mirth and beauty and music light and gay

          G7   **C**
There are frail forms waiting at the door

                           F   **C**
Though their voices are silent, their pleading looks will say

        G7   **C**
Oh hard times come again no more

CHORUS

F **C**   **G7**   **C** **F** **C**
Oh hard times come again no more

BOUND FOR SOUTH AUSTRALIA

Traditional. This arrangement by Mike Jackson.

C   G7   F

C   **G7**
In South Australia I was born, Heave away! Haul away!
C   **F**   **C**   **G7 C**
South Australia round Cape Horn, and we're bound for South Australia

CHORUS:
C   **G7**
Heave away you ruler king, Heave away! Haul away!
C   **F**   **C**   **G7 C**
Heave away you'll hear me sing, we're bound for South Australia

C   **G7**
As you wallop round Cape Horn, Heave away! Haul away!
C   **F**   **C**   **G7 C**
We wish to the Lord we'd never been born, we're bound for South Australia

CHORUS

C   **G7**
I thought I heard the old man say, Heave away! Haul away!
     C   **F**   **C**   **G7 C**
Just one more pull and then belay, We're bound for South Australia

CHORUS

Try strum no. 3 for this one.
Watch the quick change on 'Australia'.
There are only 2 beats on G7 (pick/strum)
before changing back to C

WALTZING MATILDA

Words & Music Banjo Patterson. This arrangement by Mike Jackson.

C   G7   F

C   G7   C   F
Once a jolly swagman camped by a billabong
C   G7
Under the shade of a Coolabah Tree
        C   G7
And he sang as he watched
      C   F
And waited till his billy boiled
C   G7   C
You'll come a Waltzing Matilda with me

CHORUS:
C   F
Waltzing Matilda, Waltzing Matilda
C   G7
You'll come a Waltzing Matilda with me
        C   G7
And he sang as he watched
      C   F
And waited till his billy boiled
C   G7   C
You'll come a Waltzing Matilda with me

REPEAT CHORUS

TIDDY LEND ME YOUR PIGEON

Traditional. This arrangement by Mike Jackson.

Strum no. 4 fits this song

C   G7   C G7   C
Tiddy lend me your pigeon to keep company with mine
                  G7   C G7   C
Tiddy lend me your pigeon to keep company with mine
              F   C G7   C
My pigeon's gone wild in the bush, my pigeon's gone wild,
              F   C G7   C
My pigeon's gone wild in the bush, my pigeon's gone wild

C   G7   C G7   C
Tiddy lend me your rooster to keep company with mine
                  G7   C G7   C
Tiddy lend me your rooster to keep company with mine
              F   C G7   C
My rooster's gone scratching for some corn, my rooster's gone wild
              F   C G7   C
My rooster's gone scratching for some corn, my rooster's gone wild

C   G7   C G7   C
Tiddy lend me your donkey to keep company with mine
                  G7   C G7   C
Tiddy lend me your donkey to keep company with mine
              F   C G7   C
My donkey's in the neighbour's yard, my donkey's gone wild
              F   C G7   C
My donkey's in the neighbour's yard, my donkey's gone wild

C   G7   C G7   C
Tiddy lend me your pigeon to keep company with mine
                  G7   C G7   C
Tiddy lend me your pigeon to keep company with mine

MAIRI'S WEDDING

Traditional. This arrangement by Mike Jackson.

CHORUS:

C   Am   F   G7
Step we gaily on we go, heel for heel and toe for toe
C   Am   F   G7
Arm in arm and row on row, all for Mairi's wedding

C   Am   F   G7
Over hillways up and down, myrtle green and bracken brown
C   Am   F   G7
Past the sheilings thru' the town, all for sake of Mairi

CHORUS

C   Am   F   G7
Red her cheeks as rowans are, bright her eyes as any star
C   Am   F   G7
Fairest of them all by far, is our darling Mairi

CHORUS

C   Am   F   G7
Plenty herring, plenty meal, plenty peat to fill the kreel
C   Am   F   G7
Plenty bonnie bairns as well, that's the toast for Mairi

CHORUS x 2

Practise the chord pattern first and then weave the words around the pattern
C Am F G7
//// //// //// ////

THIS TRAIN

Traditional. This arrangement by Mike Jackson.

Try this strum:

V V Λ V V Λ

down-down/up - down-down/up

or count

1 2 & 3 4 &

CHORUS:

C
This train is bound for glory this train
                                   G7
This train is bound for glory this train
C   **C7**
This train is bound for glory
F
Want to be on it you got to be holy
C   **G7**   **C**
This train is bound for glory this train

C
This train don't carry no gamblers this train
                                     G7
This train don't carry no gamblers this train
C   **C7**
This train don't carry no gamblers
F
No card players, no midnight ramblers
C   **G7**   **C**
This train don't carry no gamblers this train

CHORUS

C
This train is bound for glory this train

This train is bound for glory this train

This train is bound for glory this train

YOU ARE MY SUNSHINE

Words & Music Jimmie Davis

CHORUS:

      C   **C7**
You are my sunshine, my only sunshine

      F   **C**
You make me happy when skies are grey

      F   **C**   **Am**
You'll never know dear, how much I love you–oo

   C   **G7**   **C**
Please don't take my sunshine away

      C   **C7**
The other night dear, as I lay sleeping

     F   **C**
I dreamed I held you in my arms

     F   **C**   **Am**
When I awoke dear, I was mistaken

   C   **G7**   **C**
And I hung my head and cried

CHORUS

    C   **C7**
I'll always love you, and make you happy

     F   **C**
If you will only say the same

     F   **C**   **Am**
But if you leave me, to love another

   C **G7**   **C**
You'll regret it all some day

CHORUS

          C   **C7**
You told me once dear, you really loved me
        F   **C**
And no one else could come between
             F   **C**   **Am**
But now you've left me, and love another
        C   **G7**   **C**
You have shattered all my dreams

CHORUS

                 G7   **C**
Oh please don't take my sunshine away

MY GRANDFATHER'S CLOCK

Words & Music Henry Clay Work. This arrangement by Mike Jackson.

C   G7   F   Am

     C   G7   C   F
My grandfather's clock was too tall for the shelf
      C   G7   C
So it stood ninety years on the floor
           G7   C   F
It was taller by half than the old man himself
         C   G7   C
But it weighed not a pennyweight more
          Am   F   G7
It was bought on the morn of the day that he was born
     C   Am   F   G7
It was always his treasure and pride
     C   G7   C   F
But it stopped, short, never to go again
         C G7 C
When the old man died

CHORUS
C
Ninety years without slumbering, Tic-Toc Tic-Toc

His life's seconds numbering, Tic-Toc Tic-Toc
     C   G7   C   F
It stopped, short, never to go again
        C G7 C
When the old man died

Try strum no. 3 for this song

     C   G7   C   F
Well in watching its pendulum swing to and fro
    C   G7   C
Many hours he had spent when a boy
                    G7   C   F
And through childhood and manhood, the clock seemed to know
    C   G7   C
And to share both his grief and his joy
        Am   F   G7
For it struck twenty-four when he entered the door
    C   Am   F   G7
With a blooming and beautiful bride
    C   G7 C   F
But it stopped, short, never to go again
      C G7 C
When the old man died

CHORUS

      C   G7   C   F
Yes, it stopped, short, never to go again
      C G7 C
When the old man died

DRUNKEN SAILOR

Traditional. This arrangement by Mike Jackson.

Dm
Dm
What shall we do with a drunken sailor

C
What shall we do with a drunken sailor

Dm
What shall we do with a drunken sailor

C   **Dm**
Early in the morning!

CHORUS:

Dm
Hoo – ray and up she rises

C
Hoo – ray and up she rises

Dm
Hoo – ray and up she rises

C   **Dm**
Early in the morning

Dm
Put him in a long-boat till he's sober

C
Put him in a long-boat till he's sober

Dm
Put him in a long-boat till he's sober

C   **Dm**
Early in the morning

CHORUS

Dm
Put him in the scuppers with a hose-pipe on him

C
Put him in the scuppers with a hose-pipe on him

Dm
Put him in the scuppers with a hose-pipe on him

C   **Dm**
Early in the morning

CHORUS

MICHAEL ROW
THE BOAT ASHORE

Traditional. This arrangement by Mike Jackson.

C   F   **Dm**   G7

CHORUS:

C   F   C
Michael row the boat ashore, Hal – le – lu – yah
              Dm   C G7 C
Michael row the boat ashore, Hal – le – lu – yah

C   F   C
The river is deep, and the river is wide, Hal – le – lu – yah
                Dm   C G7 C
Greener pastures on the other side, Hal – le – lu – yah

CHORUS

C   F   C
Jordan's river is chilly and cold, Hal – le – lu – yah
            Dm   C G7 C
Chills the body but not the soul, Hal – le – lu – yah

CHORUS

WE'RE FLOATING DOWN THE RIVER

Traditional. This arrangement by Mike Jackson.

CHORUS:

C   **F**   **C**
We're floating down the river, we're floating down below

                                                      G7 F
We're floating down the river to the Ohio

C
One in the middle and you can't jump Josie

                                      F   **G7**
One in the middle and you can't get around
C
One in the middle and you can't jump Josie
F   **C**   **F**   **C**   **F**   **C**   **G7**   **C**
Hello Susan Brown. Sit down, sit down, sit down, sit down, sit down

CHORUS

C
Two in the middle and you can't jump Josie

                                      F   **G7**
Two in the middle and you can't get around
C
Two in the middle and you can't jump Josie
F   **C**   **F**   **C**   **F**   **C**   **G7**   **C**
Hello Susan Brown. Sit down, sit down, sit down, sit down, sit down

CHORUS

C
Four in the middle and you can't jump Josie

                                      F   **G7**
Four in the middle and you can't get around
C
Four in the middle and you can't jump Josie
F   **C**   **F**   **C**   **F**   **C**   **G7**   **C**
Hello Susan Brown. Sit down, sit down, sit down, sit down, sit down

Tricky last line - play two strums or each chord

PLAY ME A UKULELE TUNE

Words & Music Will Ryan.

C   Am   F   D7   G7

        C   Am   F   C
Oh won't you play me a ukulele tune
 F   **C**   **D7**   **G7**
The kind that's easy on the ears and makes you want to croon
        C   Am   F   C
Oh won't you play me a ukulele tune
    F   **C**   **G7**   **C**
I'm miraculously happy with a ukulele tune

BRIDGE:
   G7   **C**
Not a sousaphone; a slide trombone
   G7   **C**
A tuba or kazoo will ever do
          G7
Remotely what it does to me
       C   **Am   D7**   **G7**
And confidentially I'm sure it does it to you too

        C   Am   F   C
So won't you play me a ukulele tune
 F   **C**   **D7**   **G7**
The kind that's right both day and night, it's always opportune
       C   Am   F   C
For you to play me a ukulele tune
    F   **C**   **G7**   **C**
I'm incredibly contented with a ukulele tune

INSTRUMENTAL – BRIDGE

        C   Am   F   C
So won't you play me a ukulele tune
 F   **C**   **D7**   **G7**
The kind we want to hear when we're beneath the harvest moon
        C   Am   F   C
Oh won't you play me a ukulele tune
    F   **C**   **F**   **C**   **F**   **C**   **Am**
I'm miraculously happy, incredibly contented, emphatically ecstatic when I hear one
 D7   **G7**   **C**   **F C G7 C**
So please play me a ukulele tune

QUE SERA, SERA

Words & Music by Jay Livingston and Ray Evans.

C   **Cmaj7 C6**
When I was just a little boy

Cmaj7 **C**   **F** **G7**
I asked my mother, what will I be

G   **F** **G7**
Will I be handsome, will I be rich

F   **G7** **C** **C7**
Here's what she said to me

CHORUS:

   F   **C**
Que Sera, Sera, whatever will be, will be

       G   **G7**   **C G7**   **C**
The future's not ours, to see, Que Sera, Se-ra, what will be, will be

C   **Cmaj7 C6**
When I was young, I fell in love

Cmaj7 **C**   **F G7**
I asked my sweetheart what lies ahead

G   **F**   **G7**
Will we have rainbows, day after day

F   **G7** **C** **C7**
Here's what my sweetheart said

CHORUS

C   **Cmaj7 C6**
Now I have children of my own

Cmaj7   **C**   **F** **G7**
They ask their father, what will I be

G   **F**   **G7**
Will I be pretty, will I be rich

F   **G7** **C** **C7**
I tell them tenderly

CHORUS

G7   **C**
  what will be, will be

The progression of C/Cmaj7/C6/Cmaj7 is simple: place your third finger on 3rd fret A string - give 3 strums second finger on 2nd fret A string - 3 strums take finger off and play open strings - 3 strums second finger back on 2nd fret A string - 3 strums

LEANING ON A LAMP-POST

Words & Music Noel Gay. This arrangement by Mike Jackson.

C   G7   F   D7   C7

      C   **G7**   **F**   **G7**
I'm leaning on a lamp, maybe you think, I look a tramp
           C   **G7**   **C**
Or you may think I'm hanging 'round to steal a car
         G7   **F**   **G7**
But no I'm not a crook, and if you think, that's what I look
      C   **D7**   **G7**
I'll tell you why I'm here and what my motives are

(Tempo Change)
      C
I'm leaning on a lamp-post at the corner of the street
    G7   **C**
In case a certain little lady comes by
    G7 **C** **D7**   **G7**
Oh me, oh my, I hope the little lady comes by

    C
I don't know if she'll get away, she doesn't always get away
    G7   **C**
But anyhow I know that she'll try
    G7 **C** **D7**   **G7**
Oh me, oh my, I hope the little lady comes by

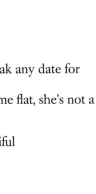

The second part has:

V V ∧

down-down/up
played very quickly on each beat
or four times per bar

                       C
There's no other girl I would wait for, but this one I'd break any date for
D7   **G7**
I won't have to ask what she's late for, she wouldn't leave me flat, she's not a girl like that

      C
Oh she's absolutely wonderful, and marvellous and beautiful
    G7   **C7**
And anyone can understand why
    F   **D7**
I'm leaning on the lamp-post on the corner of the street
      C   **G7**
In case a certain little lady comes
C   **G7**
certain little lady comes
C   **G7**   **C G7 C**
certain little lady passes by

33

UKULELE LADY

Words & Music Gus Khan and Richard A. Whiting.
This arrangement by Mike Jackson.

C   A♭7   G7   Am   Em7   F7   Cmaj7   C6   F   D7

C
                                                                 A♭7 G7 C
I saw the splendour of the moonlight, on Hono....lu....lu Bay

                                                   A♭7 G7 C
There's something tender in the moonlight, on Hono....lu....lu Bay

Am   **Em7**
And all the beaches are full of peaches, who bring their "ukes" along

C   **F7**   **G7**
And in the glimmer of the moonlight, they love to sing this song

CHORUS:
   C   Cmaj7   C6   Cmaj7   C   Cmaj7   C6   Cmaj7
If you like a Ukulele Lady, Ukulele Lady like-a-you

   F   G7   F   G7   F   G7   C
If you like to linger where it's shady Ukulele Lady linger too

   Cmaj7   C6   Cmaj7   C   Cmaj7   C6   Cmaj7
If you kiss a Ukulele Lady, While you promise ever to be true, true, true

   F   G7   F   G7   F   G7   C
And she see another Ukulele Lady fool around with you

F   **C**   **D7**   **G7**
Maybe she'll sigh – Maybe she'll cry – Maybe she'll find somebody else, Bye and bye…

   C   Cmaj7   C6   **Cmaj7   C**   **Cmaj7**   **C6   Cmaj7**
To sing to, when it's cool and shady, where the tricky Wickie Wackies woo

   F   G7   F   G7   F   G7   C
If you like a Ukulele Lady, Ukulele lady like-a-you.

C   **A♭7 G7 C**
    She used to sing to me by moonlight, on Hono....lu....lu Bay

                                            A♭7 G7 C
Fond mem'rys cling to me by moonlight, although I'm far   a–way

Am   **Em7**
Some day I'm going where eyes are glowing, and lips are made to kiss

C   **F7**   **G7**
To see somebody in the moonlight and hear the song I miss.

CHORUS

Last line of chorus – last time:

  𝔽 **G7** 𝔽   **G7** 𝔽   **G7**   **C**   **G7**   **C**   **G7**
If you like a ukulele lady, ukulele lady like a me like you, like me like you,

    C   **G7**   **C G7 C**
like me like you like you

The Que Sera, Sera chord progression of C/Cmaj7/C6/Cmaj7 is played here but with two strums per chord

HOW TO DOWNLOAD YOUR MUSIC TRACKS

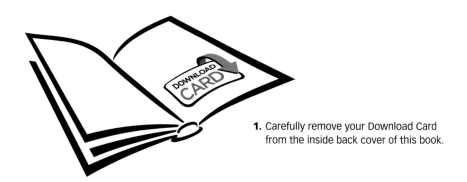

1. Carefully remove your Download Card from the inside back cover of this book.

TO REDEEM THIS CARD VISIT
www.musicsalesdownloads.com
ENTER ACCESS CODE:
XXXXXXXXXX

Download Cards are powered by Dropcards.
User must accept terms at dropcards.com/terms
which are adopted by The Music Sales Group.
Not redeemable for cash. Void where prohibited or restricted by law.

2. On the back of the card is your unique access code. Enter this at www.musicsalesdownloads.com

Opening CH81763 Recomposed by Max Richter - Vivaldi, The Four Sea...

You have chosen to open:
...763 Recomposed by Max Richter - Vivaldi, The Four Seasons.zip
which is: VLC media file (.mp3) (186 MB)
from: http://s3.amazonaws.com

What should Firefox do with this file?
Open with 7-Zip File Manager (default)
Save File
Do this automatically for files like this from now on.

OK   Cancel

3. Follow the instructions to save your files to your computer*. That's it!

*Appearance of download manager will vary depending upon operating system and web browser.
In case of difficulty when downloading files, please contact dropcards.com/help
Card missing? Please contact music@musicsales.co.uk

36